SPECIAL

Encouraging Writing

Folens
COPYMASTER

PAM TAINSH

CONTENTS

Illustrations by Eric Jones. Cover design by Abacus Art.

First published 1991 by Folens Limited, Dunstable and Dublin.

ISBN 185276287 X

Folens Limited. Apex Business Centre, Boscombe Road, Dunstable, LU5 4RL, England.

'Pupils with Special Educational Needs thrive best in a supportive language environment which is anxiety free; stimulating and rich in the varied experiences it presents.'

A Curriculum for All. National Curriculum Council 1989

This book is about writing. It arose out of concern that pupils with special educational needs do not like to write. Here are some genuine statements written by secondary school pupils about writing.

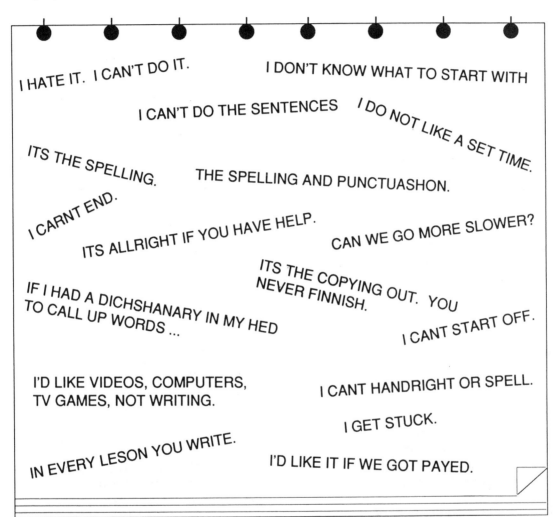

I HATE IT. I CAN'T DO IT. I DON'T KNOW WHAT TO START WITH

I CAN'T DO THE SENTENCES I DO NOT LIKE A SET TIME.

ITS THE SPELLING. THE SPELLING AND PUNCTUASHON.

I CARNT END.

ITS ALLRIGHT IF YOU HAVE HELP. CAN WE GO MORE SLOWER?

ITS THE COPYING OUT. YOU NEVER FINNISH.

IF I HAD A DICHSHANARY IN MY HED TO CALL UP WORDS ...

I CANT START OFF.

I'D LIKE VIDEOS, COMPUTERS, TV GAMES, NOT WRITING.

I CANT HANDRIGHT OR SPELL.

I GET STUCK.

IN EVERY LESON YOU WRITE.

I'D LIKE IT IF WE GOT PAYED.

There is a great deal of writing for pupils to do at secondary school, and for children having difficulties with written language the amount of writing becomes a real problem; their written work is the visible evidence of failure and low standard. Such pupils will avoid writing, or produce very little. However, even the most reluctant pupil has something to say, and something to write. The main task is to put pen to paper, get started, and produce some work; at first, any written work is better than none.

'Written work' must be taught; only rarely does it happen incidentally. What follows, in this book, are some tried and tested strategies and subjects to help teachers and pupils start improving written work. Strategies for good writing arise from speaking, listening, and looking - these skills are all part of the National Curriculum's programme of study, and form the basis of much of the work in this book.

However, there is one overriding principle and it is one which many pupils do not know, or even believe. **It is not essential to have the ideas before you write. Ideas will come as the pen moves across the page.**

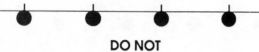

DO NOT

✗ Insist that all work is neat, accurate and fully planned
✗ Throw away the work
✗ Have long periods of silent writing
✗ Give vague starter ideas
✗ Ask for "copying out"
✗ Correct all errors
✗ Have writing every lesson
✗ Stick to the same type of format and style

DO

✔ Prepare the work
✔ Encourage daily writing
✔ Talk about writing, in groups and with partners
✔ Play games to encourage talking
✔ Free writing
✔ Write with and for the students
✔ Look at "good" writing
✔ Use different formats
✔ Use different styles
✔ Keep the work
✔ Discuss different ways to present it
✔ Make multiple copies to use as resources for students to consult
✔ Use as display
✔ Look at each other's work
✔ Proof-read, assess, use question-naire to evaluate and improve
✔ Use different types of paper
✔ Use different types of pens
✔ Use word processors

USEFUL REFERENCE BOOKS

Encouraging Writing - Robert Protherough. *Methuen (1983)*
Big Book of Optical Illusions - Gyles Brandreth. *Carousel (1979)*
Through Your Own Eyes - David and Kenneth Agar. *Oxford (1986)*
Hippogriff Feathers - Bob Stanish. *Good Apple Inc. Hamilton Press.*
Words and Their Meanings - Open University Language Development. Block 3, *Open University (1980).*
Changing Stories - English Centre, *ILEA (1984)*
Making Stories - B. Mellor, M. Raleigh and P. Ashton. English Centre, *ILEA (1984)*

I encourage pupils to write by looking at their writing as it is. We can plan how to improve it, by choosing one area at a time.

Strategies to do this should be used by all pupils not just those with special educational needs. Any strategy is better than none.

Producing written work is not only the final goal. The aim is for the pupil to be satisfied with the writing and to have enjoyed it. If that happens it must mean good teaching and good learning

'What is good practice in relation to special educational needs is good practice for all.'

NCC *A Curriculum For All.*

Encouraging Writing

Students should:

- write in a range of forms, including the following: notes, diaries, personal letters, chronological accounts, pamphlets, book reviews, advertisements, comic strips, poems, stories, playscripts.

- build on experience of a range of different stories which they have read and heard.

- handle the following elements of story structure: an opening, setting, characters, events and a resolution.

- write for a range of purposes including describing, explaining, giving instructions, reporting, expressing a point of view.

- use writing to facilitate their own thinking and learning, recognising that not all written work will lead to a polished, final product.

- record their first thoughts, capture immediate responses and collect and organise ideas so that they are available for reflection.

- write in aesthetic and imaginative ways.

- use appropriate methods of presentation for each piece of work, so that
    ✔ notes and records may be more economical and useful to themselves
    ✔ finished work is presented or displayed clearly and attractively for other readers.

PERSONAL WRITING SHEET

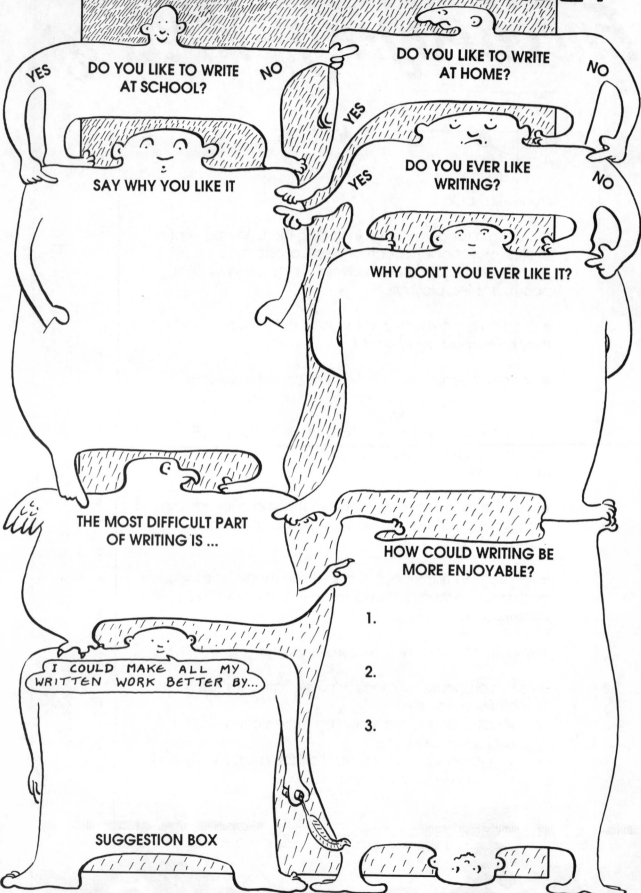

DO YOU LIKE TO WRITE AT SCHOOL?
YES — NO

SAY WHY YOU LIKE IT

DO YOU LIKE TO WRITE AT HOME?
YES — NO

DO YOU EVER LIKE WRITING?
YES — NO

WHY DON'T YOU EVER LIKE IT?

THE MOST DIFFICULT PART OF WRITING IS ...

HOW COULD WRITING BE MORE ENJOYABLE?

1.

2.

3.

I COULD MAKE ALL MY WRITTEN WORK BETTER BY...

SUGGESTION BOX

Your Writing

Fill in this sheet to show what writing you have done in the last week.

What writing?	Who for?	Why?	Type of writing?	Good/Bad/O.K.
School List	Teacher Myself	Homework Videos	Neat . Clean . Quick	Good Bad

Are you satisfied with your written work? Please tick.

Yes ☐   No ☐   Sometimes ☐

Which of these would you like to improve? Please tick:

☐	Neatness	☐	Stories
☐	Spelling	☐	Starting off
☐	Speed	☐	Grammar
☐	Style of writing	☐	Punctuation
☐	Planning	☐	Using a computer
☐	Presentation	☐	Notes

Encouraging Writing

BRAINSTORMS AND LISTING

● Brainstorming (Osborn 1963) is a method of producing a quantity of ideas in a short period of time.

● The listing technique is simply that of listing ideas associated in some way with the subject.

● Listing and brainstorming promote ideas and help written work. They can then be used with large or small groups, or with individual pupils.

● Follow these suggestions:

  ✔ write anything which comes to mind
  ✔ use a fixed amount of time
  ✔ encourage different, varied, even outlandish ideas
  ✔ go for quantity
  ✔ develop ideas from other ideas
  ✔ list after the brainstorm
  ✔ use listing to sort out good ideas.

● Summary:

A

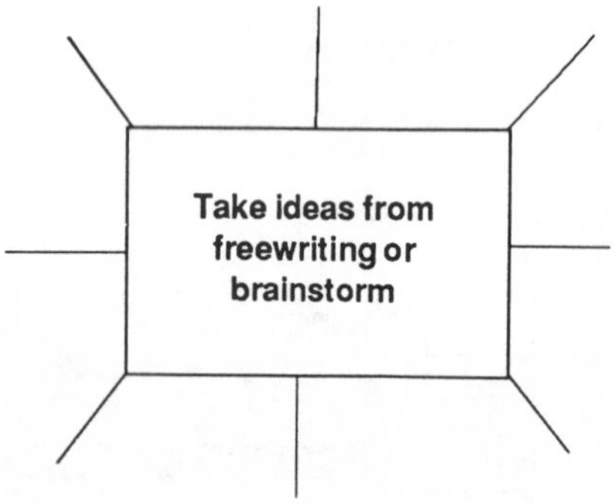

Take ideas from freewriting or brainstorm

B

Sort into a list
1.
2.
3.
4.
5.

C

Plan of writing:	1
2	3

BRAINSTORMING

This is a way to start to write.

Choose any subject.

Write as much as possible about it on the back of this sheet.

TAKE 3 MINUTES.

Jackie's example.

Vijay's example.

HUNGER → STARVING
CANTONESE → FRENCH → ITALIAN → INDIAN
SCHOOL
CHINESE
MEALS
CHIPS AND FISH → KETCHUP → SALT VINEGAR
MIDNIGHT SNACKS
CALORIES
FOOD
DIET
NOUVEAU CUISINE
FAT OBESE
THROW UP
RESTAURANTS
OVEREATING
TAKE AWAY
EAT IN
FAST FOOD

CARROTS ARE SUPPOSED TO MAKE YOU SEE IN THE DARK
ADDITIVES
VITAMIN C
FISH IS GOOD FOR THE BRAIN
MY FAVOURITE FRUIT IS APPLE → I LIKE BANANAS
YOU NEED CALORIES
FOOD
SUGAR ROTS TEETH
CABBAGE IS GOOD FOR YOU → GREENS ARE GOOD FOR YOU
WHOLEMEAL BREAD IS GOOD FOR YOU → WHITE BREAD IS NOT SO GOOD
MILK CONTAINS CALCIUM
CALCIUM IS GOOD FOR YOU

NOW BRAINSTORM BELOW ABOUT MONEY

THE SPELLING MISTAKES CAN BE CORRECTED LATER.

Look how these words have made her think of other words.

COINS
MONEY

BRAINSTORM
● clothes
● friends
● blood

LISTS

Making lists is a way of helping you think.

MAKE A LIST OF:

Things I like ...

What I watch on TV ...

COMPLAINTS AND SUGGESTIONS

What is boring?

What is frightening?

Who annoys you? Why?

Could you change it?

What is dangerous?

Who could stop it?

TALK ABOUT...
- What did you think of first? last?
- How did you think of what to write?
- How did you decide you had finished the list?

WRITE ON THE BACK OF THIS SHEET.

Write lists of things ...   ... to take on holiday to Spain.   ... to do before a party.

You could write a short passage here ...

This page may be photocopied for classroom use only

WASHING MY HAIR

BRAINSTORM around this head.

FREE WRITING

This is a way to put ideas down on paper. It is similar to brainstorming and listing.

- Write anything.
- Write for 3 minutes. Do not stop.
- Use a large piece of paper.
- Choose a subject from this page.

Going down a waterslide ...

Going to the dentist ...

Taking off in a plane ...

A video ...

The fair ...

Eating jelly with chopsticks ...

- STOP
- CHECK IT
- CROSS OUT
- SAVE THE BEST PARTS
- REWRITE, USING WORDS YOU HAVE KEPT

WORD ASSOCIATION

What does the word **KNIFE** make you think about?

FOOD? FORK? MURDER? KITCHEN? CUTTING?

or something else? Write down the first words that come to mind.

Look at these words.

HOT AIR BALLOON

ISLAND

TELEPHONE

Write down words they make you think of.

UP

WRITE ON THE DOTTED LINES.

Now write an advert using your words.

GET UP AND GO IN THIS SUPERB HOT AIR BALLOON.

Write down the first word you think of when you read ...

pair
night
brain
party
water
video

treasure
watch
hill
blood
volcano
holiday

Now put your ideas together to start writing.

Encouraging Writing

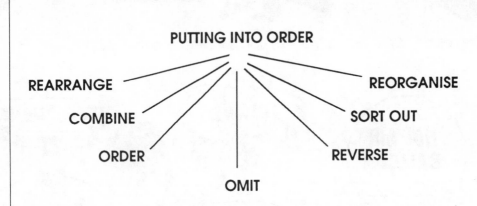

PUTTING INTO ORDER

REARRANGE   REORGANISE

COMBINE   SORT OUT

ORDER   REVERSE

OMIT

- 'Sequencing' is a necessary skill in written work, not only for story beginnings, middles, and ends, but as a strategy to improve the style and clarity of the language.

- Many pupils with literacy problems are unable to order their thoughts and words.

- Rearranging and sorting out follow on from brainstorms, lists, associations and free writing: the 'ordering' is the next stage towards drafting.

- The following activities are to do with ordering. Firstly, writing sequences from ongoing experience: eating a sweet. Secondly, a sequence of a set of actions to solve a problem, 'Eating an Egg'.

- Sequencing the work is part of sorting out ideas.

- Pupils must try to accept that:

     ✔ usually nothing is perfect first time
     ✔ rough notes are important
     ✔ rough notes are meant to have mistakes and be untidy
     ✔ rough work has to be sorted out
     ✔ putting in order is starting to draft and look for errors
     ✔ the final copy is the one that counts.

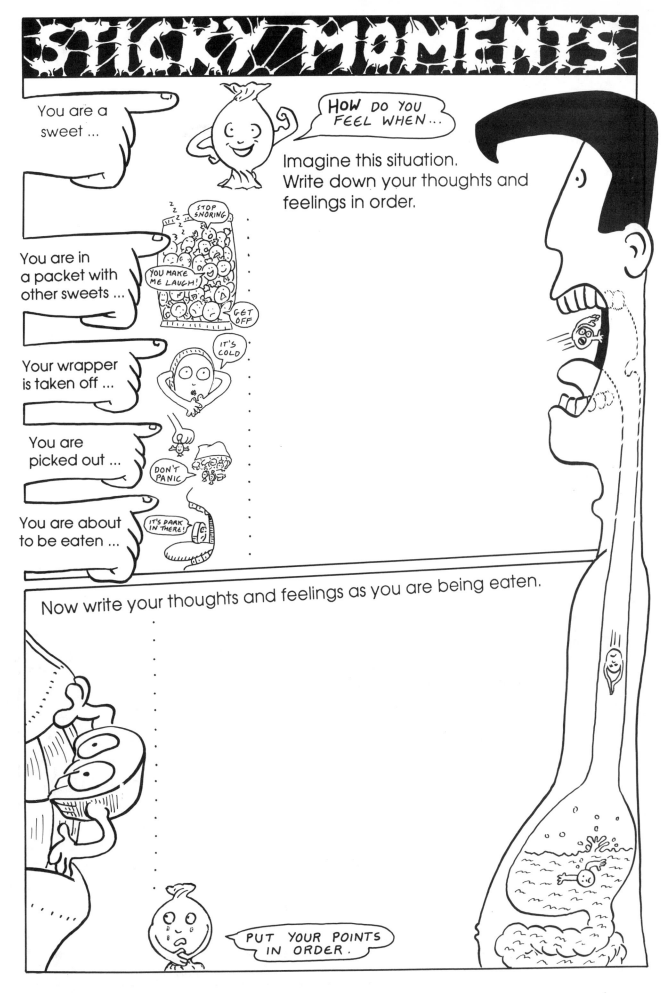

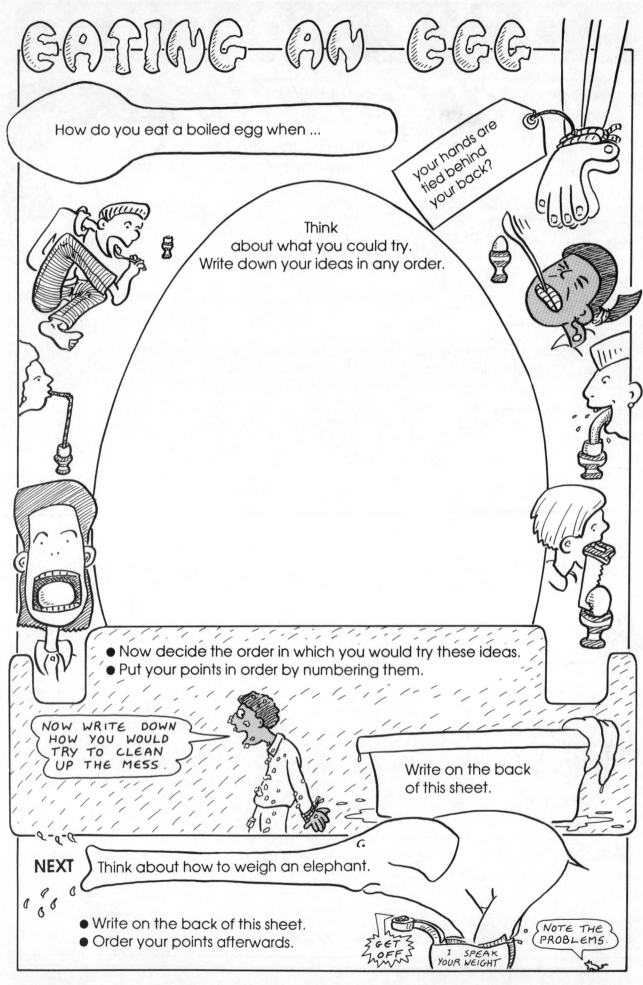

EATING AN EGG

How do you eat a boiled egg when ...

your hands are tied behind your back?

Think about what you could try. Write down your ideas in any order.

- Now decide the order in which you would try these ideas.
- Put your points in order by numbering them.

NOW WRITE DOWN HOW YOU WOULD TRY TO CLEAN UP THE MESS.

Write on the back of this sheet.

NEXT Think about how to weigh an elephant.

- Write on the back of this sheet.
- Order your points afterwards.

GET OFF

I SPEAK YOUR WEIGHT

NOTE THE PROBLEMS.

Encouraging Writing

TALKING AND WRITING

● Pupil talk is a very good way to encourage ideas for written work.

● If no time is given for preparation, talking is a type of verbal brainstorm. Encourage pupils to give 'on the spot' 'off the record' talks for one or two minutes: always give a title, and instruct them to say anything which comes to mind, even if it is unrelated.

● Such talk becomes starting points for further group talk, which in turn leads to ideas. All Key Stage 3 pupils begin to 'give talks' as part of English examination requirements, so these activities practice talking, listening and writing.

● The following activities are ways to encourage such skills. A talk on 'my favourite meal' is a good starter, as pupils always have something to say - see page 20; similarly, the 'Moan Phone'. It is important, at this stage, not to prepare the talk; such preparatory work can cause anxiety; on the spot talking is fun, particularly if pupils give the teacher a subject as well.

● Giving interviews is a good way to encourage talking and writing; interviewing is 'direct experience' to gain ideas. However, interviewing should not degenerate into a routine boring format.

● Strategies of 'free talking', 'brainstorms', and role play are entertaining, particularly if conducted with the use of an 'artist' to do quick sketches of the interviewee. These sketches can be done on a board, or paper, and then, if appropriate, photocopied. These can then be used to attach to the interview record or to generate further writing activities.

HAPPY EATER

Talking about things helps to give you ideas for writing.

Talk about your favourite meal.

Each take 1 minute.

TAKE IT IN TURNS.

My favourite meal.

Answer these questions.

- Where would you eat it? _____
- Would you be alone or with friends? _____
- Who would cook it? _____
- Could you cook it? _____
- What would you need? _____
  _____
- Would it be good for you? _____

Do the talk again. Each take 2 minutes.

TALK ABOUT...

- Did you have more to say this time?
- What were your group's best ideas?

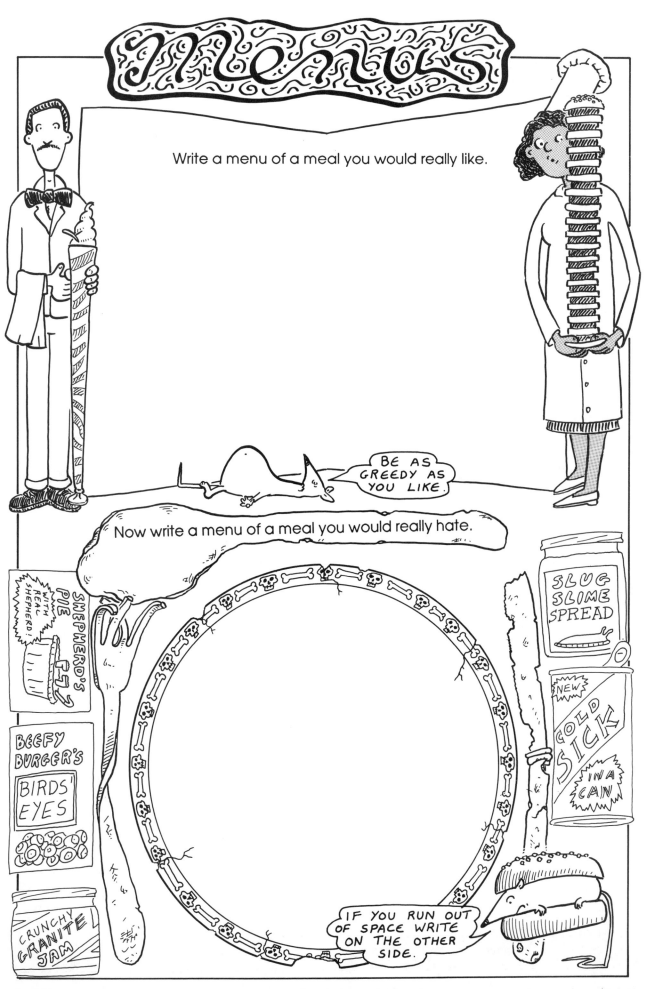

Menus

Write a menu of a meal you would really like.

BE AS GREEDY AS YOU LIKE

Now write a menu of a meal you would really hate.

SHEPHERD'S PIE WITH REAL SHEPHERD!

SLUG SLIME SPREAD

BEEFY BURGER'S BIRDS' EYES

NEW COLD SICK IN A CAN

CRUNCHY GRANITE JAM

IF YOU RUN OUT OF SPACE WRITE ON THE OTHER SIDE.

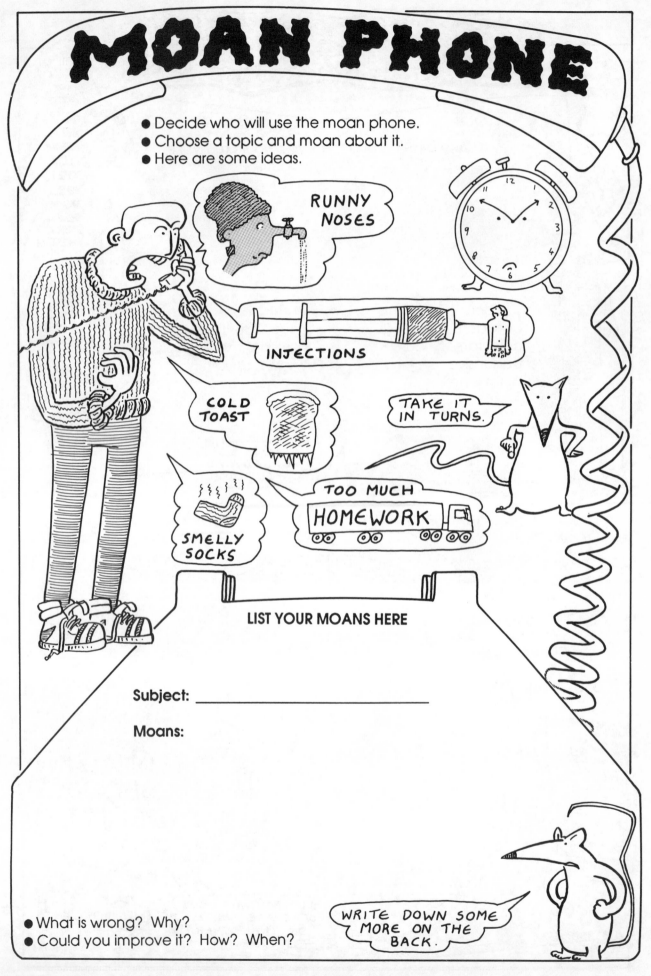

MOAN PHONE

- Decide who will use the moan phone.
- Choose a topic and moan about it.
- Here are some ideas.

RUNNY NOSES

INJECTIONS

COLD TOAST

TAKE IT IN TURNS.

SMELLY SOCKS

TOO MUCH HOMEWORK

LIST YOUR MOANS HERE

Subject: _____

Moans:

- What is wrong? Why?
- Could you improve it? How? When?

WRITE DOWN SOME MORE ON THE BACK.

FIRST IMPRESSIONS

- Cut out **A** and **B**. - Choose a partner.

Read out **A**.

This person is energetic, confident, talks a lot, cold, rather inquisitive, persuasive.
What is he like?

This person is energetic, confident, talks a lot, warm, rather inquisitive, persuasive.
What is he like?

Ask your partner to write a character description of A.

Character description.

Hobbies?

Friends?

Popular?

Good fun?

Trustworthy?

Helpful?

Hardworking?

Some help.

Choose another partner.
Read out **B**.
Ask this partner to write about person **B**.

TALK ABOUT...

All 3 of you look at the descriptions.
- Are they similar?
- Any differences?
- What has caused all the differences?
- Can you judge a person from a few words?

FACE TO FACE

Each choose one of these three roles.

DON'T FORGET THE INTERVIEW SHEET.

- You will ask questions from the interview sheet.
- You will write down the answers.

INTERVIEWER

INTERVIEWEE

- You will answer questions about yourself.

- You will sketch the interviewee.
- Try to show how they feel.
- The drawings can be very simple.

ARTIST

USE A BIG SHEET OF PAPER.

- Now all look at the interview sheet.
- You could write down some of your own questions on it.
- Begin the interview.

TALK ABOUT...

- Were the answers truthful on your interview sheet?
- Did you learn anything new about the interviewee?

- On the artist's pictures, was the interviewee ...

NERVOUS?   CONFIDENT?   RELAXED?   SHY?   CONCENTRATING?

NEXT CHOOSE A DIFFERENT ROLE AND HAVE ANOTHER INTERVIEW.

FACE TO FACE
INTERVIEW SHEET

Name of interviewer:

Name of interviewee:

QUESTIONS	ANSWERS
What is your name?	
How old are you?	
Where do you live?	
What do you look like?	
What are you like?	
What are you good at?	
What can't you do?	
What would you like to be?	
What are you interested in?	
Do you like school?	

Write your own.

SCHOOL REPORT

Choose an adult ...

You could choose
- ✔ a parent
- ✔ your teacher
- ✔ your neighbour

BASHER

DON'T FORGET THE 'SCHOOL REPORT' INTERVIEW SHEET.

... and a school friend to interview.

Look at the school report interview sheet.
- ● Write down some more questions about your school.
- ● Include questions about:

SCHOOL UNIFORM

EQUIPMENT AND RESOURCES

P E

BOOKS AND THE LIBRARY

EXAM RESULTS

TEACHING

SCHOOL TRIPS

MUSIC

- ● Interview one person at a time.
- ● Write on the interview sheet.
- ● Draw sketches of the interviewees.

YOU HAVE NOW WRITTEN A PLAN.

- ● Using the information you have collected, write about your school
- ● Include all views and opinions.
- ● Use a typewriter, a word processor or your best handwriting.

SCHOOL REPORT

INTERVIEW SHEET

Name of interviewer:

ADULT

SCHOOL FRIEND

Draw sketches
of interviewees

What is your name?
What is your job?

Now write
your own
questions.

THE BEHAVING GAME

This game can be about any type of behaving. Here are some situations.

In the bathroom

At an interview

On the beach

In a restaurant

In a favourite lesson

At the cinema

Visiting your friends

Doing homework

Visiting your parents' friends

On Christmas Day

In an exam you can do

In an exam you cannot do

Going around the shops

In a car going too fast

On a roller coaster

● Cut out the cards and put them face down.
● Ask someone to choose two.
● Interview your partner. How would **they** behave in the situations?

✔ Ask about small details
✔ Ask about feelings
✔ Make sure about the order of the behaviour
✔ Write down the answers as notes
✔ Write a piece called: *How to Behave when ...*

Encouraging Writing

LOOK AND WRITE

● We have thoughts about everything we see. These thoughts, can be expressed as either a straightforward description or an imaginative story.

● However, it is not particularly useful to show a pupil an apple, with an instruction 'describe it'. The result could be 'it is green, you eat it'. The main problem is to extend and develop the writing from a single sentence to a piece of work of acceptable length and standard.

● Showing any visual stimuli is a good starting point; use the strategies of:

    ✔ brainstorming
    ✔ listing
    ✔ ordering
    ✔ combining
    ✔ reversing
    ✔ free writing
    ✔ word association

to find things to say and to reorganise the writing.

● The following activities are all based on visuals. "Can You Look" provides examples of looking, describing and developing written work.

● "Look Again" are activities based on well known visual illusion drawings; tried and tested, this work always guarantees a responsive interested audience.

● "Look Twice" are activities developed from projective material; ink blots, blurred figures and confused imprecise pictures.

● The activities should provide discussion, comparison of work and good writing.

It helps you to write when you have something in front of you to look at.

THINK OF SOMEONE YOUR PARTNER WILL RECOGNIZE...

IT COULD BE A...

FRIEND...

TEACHER...

POP STAR...

T.V. PERSONALITY...

?

DO NOT TELL YOUR PARTNER WHO IT IS.

Describe their ...

HAIR
FOREHEAD
EYEBROWS.
CREASES
EARS
EYES
CHEEKS
NOSE
MOUTH
CHIN

GIVE YOUR PARTNER TIME TO DRAW A FEATURE BEFORE DESCRIBING THE NEXT ONE.

Think about:
● colour
● shape
● size
● texture.

Your partner should draw the face here.

ASK your partner to guess who it is.

NOW YOUR PARTNER MUST DESCRIBE A FACE FOR YOU TO DRAW. GUESS WHO IT IS.

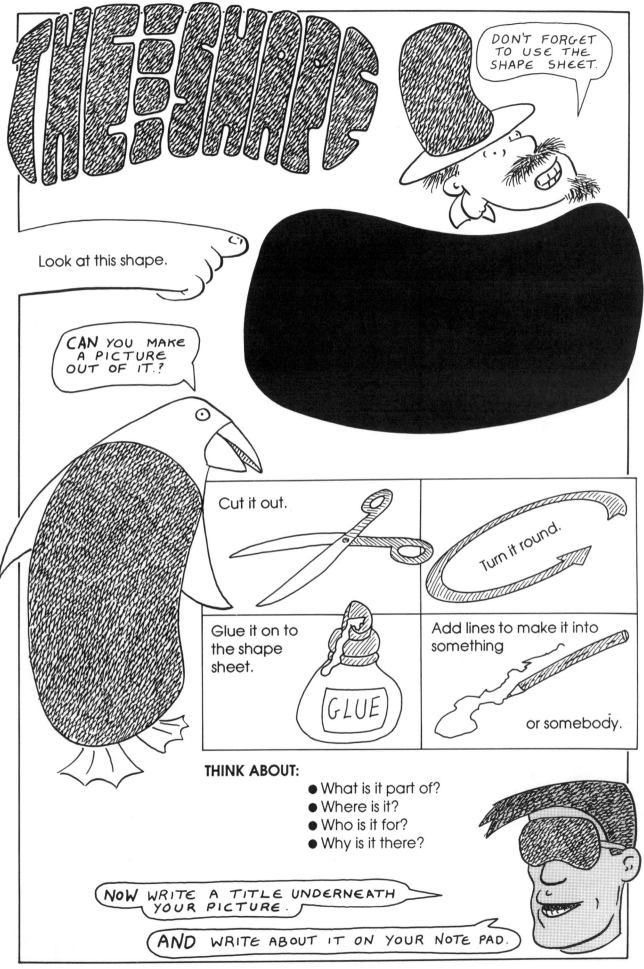

THE SHAPE SHEET

Title here

Sign here

NOTES

CONTINUE TO WRITE ON THE BACK OF THIS SHEET.

CAN YOU LOOK?

How do these people feel?

Write here _____

_____

Which person do you think is the cleverest? Draw a circle round her.

- Is it true that people who wear glasses are clever?
- Do all clever people wear glasses and smile?
- Is it true that fatter people are happier?
- Do you know a happy, thin person?

DRAW THE FACE OF A PERSON YOU CAN SEE.

What does the face tell you about:

✔ their mood?

✔ their personality?

✔ how hardworking they are?

Do these 3 things tell you what a person is like?

HAIR

CLOTHES

JOB

YES NO

Should you judge a person by the way they look? Why?

LOOK AGAIN

Not everything is as it first appears.

AM I A BIRD?

OR A RABBIT?

The brain tries to make sense of what is there.
It puts meaning into what we see.

DRAW A CARROT NEAR THE PICTURE.

WHAT DIFFERENCE DOES IT MAKE?

Look at these.

A

B

C

WRITE EVERYTHING YOU SEE. DO YOU EVER SEE MORE THAN ONE PICTURE?

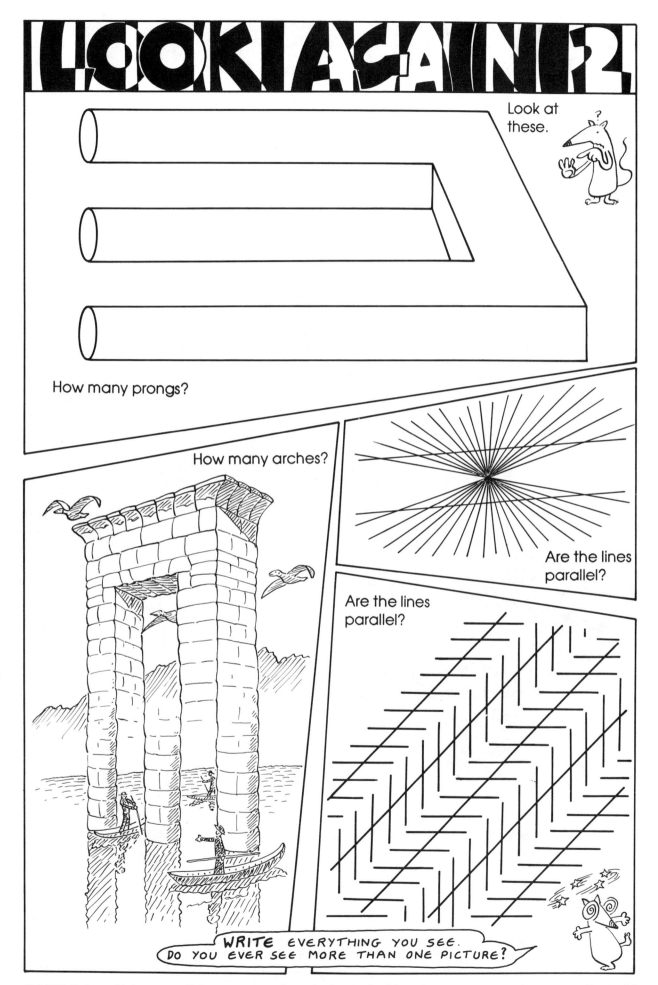

Look at these.

How many prongs?

How many arches?

Are the lines parallel?

Are the lines parallel?

WRITE EVERYTHING YOU SEE. DO YOU EVER SEE MORE THAN ONE PICTURE?

LOOK TWICE

What can you see in this strange picture?

Can you see any animals, birds or insects?

Use all of the picture.

Or just a part of it.

Turn it round.

Look at it closely.

Hold it far away.

Write down your ideas here.	Write down 8 words that you are reminded of.
Bird	
Like this	

NOW ASK YOUR PARTNER TO PRODUCE AN INK BLOT.

WRITE DOWN WHAT YOU CAN SEE ON THE BACK OF THIS SHEET.

WRITE DOWN SOME WORDS THAT YOU ARE REMINDED OF.

What can you see in this strange picture?

Use all of the picture.

Can you see any animals, birds or insects?

Or just a part of it.

Hold it far away.

Turn it round.

Look at it closely.

NOW WHAT ABOUT THIS?

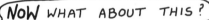

- Is it a boy, a girl, an adult?
- Is the person angry, calm, sad?
- Can you say if the person is beautiful, fit, healthy?
- Think of some other words to describe the picture.
- Write down any associations you may have to the words.

WORDS	ASSOCIATIONS

Encouraging Writing

MORE IMAGINATIVE WRITING

● To be 'instructed' to write a story about anything you wish is not a treat for most pupils who have problems with literacy.

● However, students at Key Stage 3 for English are expected to "handle story structure" with beginnings, middles and endings. It is for this type of work that strategies of brainstorming, associations, free writing, lists and sequencing are so helpful; they precede the drafting, providing good starting points.

● The following activities are 'starters for creative writing'. 'Nasties' are visuals with morbid suggestions which usually provoke comment and imaginative written work.

● 'Oddities' are similar; they provide a visual to encourage reactions, words and stories.

● All too often pupils have trouble with beginnings, or they make the middle go on for ever, or fail to achieve a good ending. Story writing is definitely difficult, but if all three stages are practised using well known stories, plot charts and plans, the written work may improve.

● Activities along these lines are included in the next part of this collection. Hopefully they, and others similar, will encourage more confidence with creative written work.

NASTIES

CHOOSE ONE OF THESE NASTY SITUATIONS...

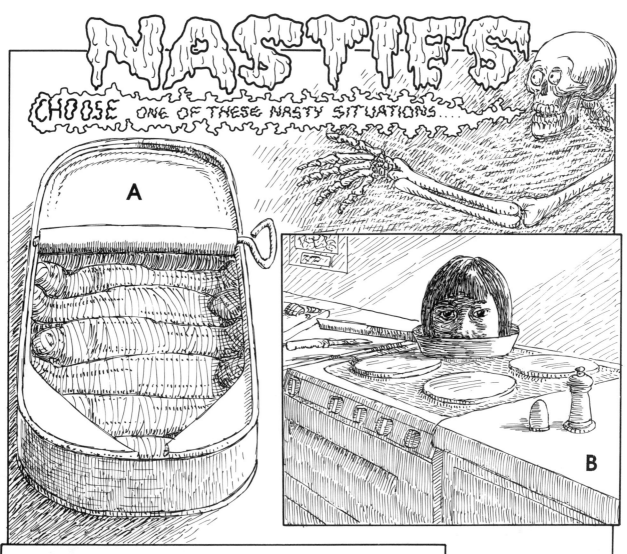

A

B

C

- Write down all your thoughts and feelings about the situation.

- Draw circles around your best ideas.

- Add more details and description to these.

- Cross out anything that is boring.

- Order your ideas.

- Write something that is really interesting!

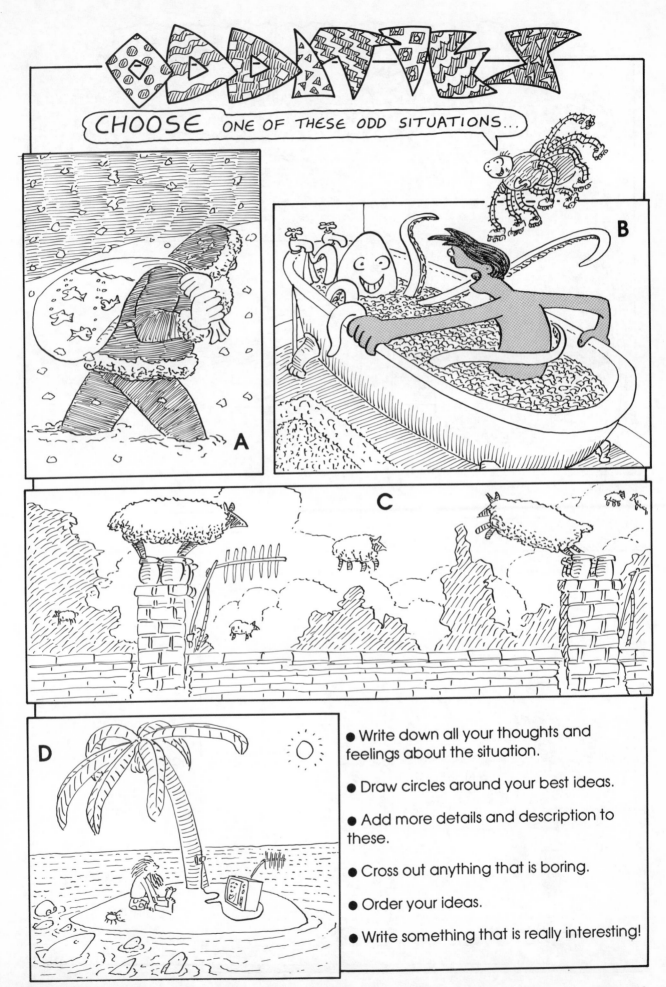

ODDITIES

CHOOSE ONE OF THESE ODD SITUATIONS...

- Write down all your thoughts and feelings about the situation.

- Draw circles around your best ideas.

- Add more details and description to these.

- Cross out anything that is boring.

- Order your ideas.

- Write something that is really interesting!

WHAT IS A STORY?

What types of stories are there?

LOOK THE PICTURES WILL HELP.

Think of some different settings.

Draw and describe some story characters in the boxes.

● Now think of a good story that you have read.

Write down:

Title: _____

Author: _____

Was it funny?   exciting?   mysterious?   thrilling? _____

Would you recommend it? _____

This page may be photocopied for classroom use only

STORY BEGINNINGS

Can you tell what a story is going to be about from its first page?

He held the gun up to the window.

- What sort of story will this be?
- What will happen?
- Would you enjoy reading it?

Write about what sort of stories you would find these two characters in. What do you think will happen to them?

There are 7 more story characters on the bottom of this page.
- What sort of story will they be found in?
- What do you think will happen to them?
- You could write your ideas on the back of this sheet.

AN UGLY FROG.

A STEPMOTHER.

A JOLLY GIANT.

A BRUTAL SOLDIER.

A LITTLE GREEN MAN.

A MASKED LADY.

A QUIETLY SPOKEN COWBOY.

WRITE ON THE BACK OF THIS SHEET.

OPENING SENTENCES

Where do all these opening sentences come from?
You could write your answers on the back of this sheet.

① Answer three questions, at least one from Part A.

② FREE GIFT INSIDE "THE GHOST PEOPLE" A GREAT COMPETITION

③ The street was deserted. Footsteps came nearer. Menacing.

④ THE COUNTRY'S FIRST AND BEST CAR DEALER

⑤ I am 18 years old. I have 7 G.C.S.E. subjects. I am interested in....

⑥ Her heart beat faster. He walked towards her, smiling.

⑦ I WAS BORN ON 22 MAY 1973 IN A SMALL TOWN CALLED...

⑧ Dear Parents, This has been a short term but the school has done ....

⑨ Two men watched, guns ready, radios in contact ...

⑩ To make the base sieve the flour ...

⑪ It had red eyes and enormous teeth. The children froze in fear ...

⑫ Got up. Washed. Had Breakfast. Met Vicky at the shops.

⑬ Once upon a time there was a princess...

⑭ TO OPEN PUSH BACK WINGS TO FULL EXTENT

⑮ It came to pass on the seventh day, a man called John, leader of ...

⑯ Take 3 each day for 7 days.

⑰ Watch out for extra work this week. A friend will ask for help.

⑱ YZR2 calling. Approaching Venus. Re-entry 1300 hours. Countdown.

⑲ DAILY MOON POISON FAILS TO STOP RATS An army of rats have | and then the rats

⑳ I LOVE YOU... YES I DO... I LOVE YOU... BOO-HOO-HOO...

Each write an opening sentence for:
- a menu
- a get well card
- an experiment
- video instructions
- a love letter

Cut out your sentences and muddle them up.

THE REST OF THE GROUP MUST DECIDE WHICH ONE IS WHICH

TALK ABOUT ONE SENTENCE AT A TIME
- IS IT INTERESTING? CLEAR? FUNNY?
- WHAT WOULD YOU WRITE NEXT?

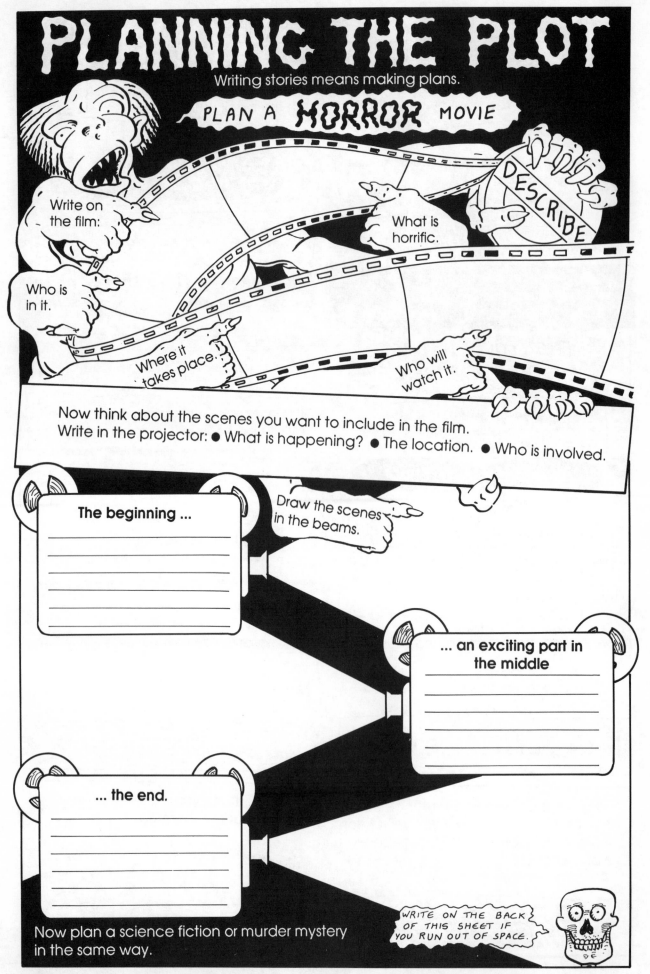

PLANNING THE PLOT

Writing stories means making plans.

PLAN A HORROR MOVIE

Write on the film:

Who is in it.

Where it takes place.

What is horrific.

DESCRIBE

Who will watch it.

Now think about the scenes you want to include in the film.
Write in the projector: ● What is happening? ● The location. ● Who is involved.

Draw the scenes in the beams.

The beginning ...

... an exciting part in the middle

... the end.

Now plan a science fiction or murder mystery in the same way.

WRITE ON THE BACK OF THIS SHEET IF YOU RUN OUT OF SPACE.

THE JACK PLOT

Read this or listen to someone reading it.

Write here.

Lazy Jack lives with his mother. They are very poor and they have to sell their animals to get food.

All they have left is one cow. Jack's mother tells him to take the cow to market and sell it. On the way, Lazy Jack meets a man who offers him some magic beans for the cow. Jack could not be bothered to walk to the market so he takes the beans. His mother is furious: she hurls the beans into the garden. Overnight a huge beanstalk grows up and up into the clouds. Lazy Jack climbs up it, and finds it is the pathway to a castle. The castle is full of gold, but it is the home of a Giant.

Jack puts the gold in his pockets, but is so stupid and slow that he is caught. The Giant puts him in a birdcage and makes him dance, juggle and do cart-wheels all day. The Giant takes Jack to fairs and festivals and Jack has to dance on a little round stage and other Giants pay to watch him.

Jack's new owner gets more and more money from making Lazy Jack work all day and Jack gets very tired. The Giant sends some of the money down the stalk to Jack's mother, who is glad to know that her lazy son is at last working hard for his living, and at last helping her to buy food and more cows.

Write an order of the events which happened.

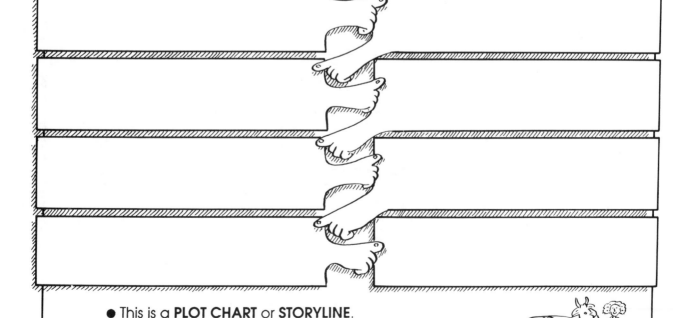

- This is a **PLOT CHART** or **STORYLINE**.
- It could be changed into a diary.
- Write a day's diary entry for either Jack or the Giant.

This page may be photocopied for classroom use only

NEW ENDINGS

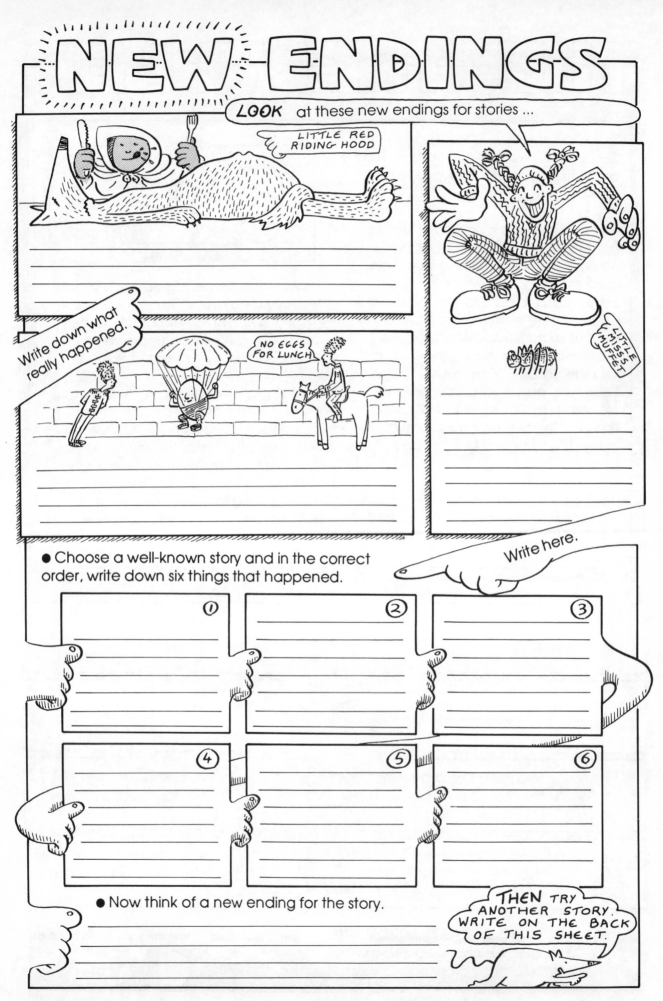

LOOK at these new endings for stories ...

LITTLE RED RIDING HOOD

Write down what really happened.

NO EGGS FOR LUNCH

LITTLE MISS MUFFET

Write here.

● Choose a well-known story and in the correct order, write down six things that happened.

① ② ③

④ ⑤ ⑥

● Now think of a new ending for the story.

THEN TRY ANOTHER STORY. WRITE ON THE BACK OF THIS SHEET.

THE STORY GAME

● Talk about all the different kinds of story and fill in this table.

Type of story	Type of characters?	Type of events?
FAIRY		
COWBOY		
HORROR		
ADVENTURE THRILLER		
BIBLE		
ROMANCE		
SCIENCE FICTION		

TO PLAY, YOU NEED THE STORY GAME CHART.
  Throw the dice:
  ✔ first for your box in column **A**, 1 to 6
  ✔ second for your box in column **B**, 1 to 6
  ✔ third for your box in coumn **C**, 1 to 6
  ✔ fourth for your box in column **D**, 1 to 6
● You should now have all the information - kind of story, the people, places and events - so you can now write your own short story.
● You will need to make up your own ending.

YOU NEED A DICE AND THE STORY GAME CHART.

THE STORY GAME CHART

A TYPE OF STORY	B SETTING	C CHARACTERS	D EVENTS	E ENDING?
1. HORROR	Town. House. Castle.	Dracula. Animals. Vampires. Ghosts.	Death. Chases.	?
2. SCIENCE FICTION	Space. Lab. Underwater.	Astronaut. Diver. Professor.	Travel. Flights. Experiments.	?
3. ROMANCE	School. Offices. Disco. Party. Hospital.	Man. Woman. Boy. Girl. Teacher. Friend. Filmstar. Doctor.	Parties. Break-ups. Dates. Discos. Weddings.	?
4. ADVENTURE	Desert. Forest. Temples. Jungle. Sea. Tombs. Lost cities.	Hero. Heroine. Baddies. Villains. Ghosts.	Murders. Chases. Discoveries. Escapes. Captures.	?
5. FAIRY	Castle. Garden. Cave.	Princess. Prince. Fairy Godmother. Elves. Witches.	Spells. Kidnaps. Deaths.	?
6. WESTERN	Desert. Ranch. Frontier town. Saloon bar. Barber's shop. Jail.	Baddies. Cowboys. Indians. Sheriff.	Chases. Break-outs. Gunfights. Duels. Death.	?